AT THE CENTER OF THE UNIVERSE, AT THE BEGINNING AND END OF ALL CREATION, SITS THE PLANET OF **Vermonia**, RULED BY QUEEN FRASINELLA.

ALL WORLDS, INCLUDING THE FRAGILE BLUE STAR, ORBIT AROUND HER, FOLLOWING PATHWAYS OF THE NET BETWEEN GALAXIES, WHEREIN THE TURTLE REALM ALSO LIES.

As the final battle rages, and Lord Boros suffers defeat at the hands of his brother, Queen Frasinella gathers her four most trusted ministers. She uses her magic to transform them, then bids them to flee in order to safeguard the wisdom of her world and to work for its rebirth.

As her final sovereign act, Queen Frasinella summons from deep within her the four Veras of her spirit. These four will be reborn on a distant planet as four warriors who will one day restore her reign of harmony.

VERMONIA

Quest for the Silver Tiger

YOYO

WALKER
BOOKS

FIRST PUBLISHED IN 2009 BY WALKER BOOKS LTD
87 VAUXHALL WALK, LONDON SE11 5HJ

2 4 6 8 10 9 7 5 3 1

COPYRIGHT © 2009 RAITETSU MEDIA LLC AND RAY PRODUCTIONS LTD
NEW YORK AND TOKYO

THE RIGHT OF RAITETSU MEDIA LLC AND RAY PRODUCTIONS LTD TO BE JOINTLY IDENTIFIED
AS AUTHORS OF THIS WORK HAS BEEN ASSERTED BY THEM IN ACCORDANCE WITH THE
COPYRIGHT, DESIGNS AND PATENTS ACT 1988

THIS BOOK HAS BEEN TYPESET IN CCLADRONN ITALIC

PRINTED AND BOUND IN CHINA

BRITISH LIBRARY CATALOGUING IN PUBLICATION DATA: A CATALOGUE RECORD FOR THIS
BOOK IS AVAILABLE FROM THE BRITISH LIBRARY

MY QUEEN, THE ARMY OF LORD BOROS HAS BEEN DEFEATED.

GENERAL URO WILL BREACH THE PALACE DEFENSES WITHIN THE HOUR.

THANK YOU, RAITETSU.

死神

A SQUELP IS SUCH A FRAGILE THING.

GO FORTH INTO THE TURTLE REALM!

MIGHTY GUARDIANS OF VERMONIA!

YOU TOO MUST TRANSFORM, JUST AS ALL THAT IS BEST IN OUR KINGDOM MUST NOW CHANGE.

VERMONIA EXISTS NOT JUST IN SPACE BUT ALSO THROUGH YOUR INTENTIONS.

NOW GO, MY TRUSTED MINISTERS. BE FAITHFUL TO OUR KINGDOM AND OUR IDEALS.

I SHALL FOLLOW YOUR ORDERS TO THE LETTER, YOUR MAJESTY. THIS EGG WILL NOT BREAK, NOR WILL IT HATCH UNTIL ITS TIME.

I MUST HURRY. URO'S SOLDIERS ARE ALREADY IN PURSUIT OF THE FOUR MINISTERS.

I MUST GO TO BLUE STAR.

HEY, ZANNI!

READ THE SIGN.

I'M TELLING YOU HOW IT IS!

AH... Mel

YOU CAN'T KEEP ME OUT!

TYPICAL. NAOMI AND MEL ARE AT IT AGAIN.

THIS HAS TO BE SOMEBODY'S IDEA OF A BAD JOKE.

NO TRESPASSING BY ORDER OF THE UNION CITY MAYOR'S OFFICE

SO IT'S TRUE WHAT MY MOM SAID. THE MAYOR WANTS TO SELL THIS LOT.

AND I THOUGHT MEL'S DAD LIKED SKATE ZOMBIES.

YOU WISH, MAN.

MY DAD SAID SOMETHING ABOUT IT TOO.

YEAH, AND PEOPLE ARE SAYING HE WANTS TO SELL THE LOT NEXT DOOR AS WELL.

THAT'S SO CRAZY. I DON'T GET IT.

WHY CAN'T HE JUST BUILD US A SKATE PARK? EVERY OTHER CITY HAS ONE.

WHATEVER.

TOP

夏 28

WHAT A WIPEOUT! HE REALLY BIT IT.

OUCH!

oh!

Ouch!

HERE—PUT THIS ON YOUR CUT.

ARE YOU OK? CALM DOWN.

Ah

NO PROBLEM. NOW YOU'RE AN OFFICIAL MEMBER OF VERACITY'S FAN CLUB.

COOL. THANKS A LOT.

THANKS, DUDE.

WE'RE GONNA TRY.

I HOPE YOU GUYS WIN. YOU ROCK!

Thanks Naomi!

WE'LL WIN. WE'RE VERACITY, THE GREATEST BAND THERE IS.

I DON'T KNOW, BUT LOADS.

Naomi's so cool!!

NAOMI, THE BATTLE OF THE BANDS IS IN, LIKE, THREE WEEKS.

HOW MUCH DID YOU SAY THE PRIZE MONEY WAS?

ENTRIES MUST BE IN BY JUNE 10TH.

AT 5:00 P.M.

MINORS HAVE TO GET THEIR PARENTS' PERMISSION. MUST BE A LACKAWAKA COUNTY RESIDENT, YADA YADA YADA...

OK. WE'VE GOT IT COVERED.

LET'S DO IT!

DOUG ON DRUMS.

FIRST PRIZE IS OURS! VERACITY RULES.

JIM ON BASS, NAOMI ON LEAD.

MEL ON KEYBOARD AND SINGING "STEP UP".

BUT...

YEAH, MEL'S QUIT THE BAND.

THAT'S A PROBLEM....

THAT'S WHAT YOU THINK?

TAKE IT EASY, MEL!

JIM SAID YOU WERE GOING TO FALL ON YOUR FACE.

HAHAHA

WELL?

WELL WHAT?

JUST WATCH.

A LOT OF BIG TALK.

LET'S SEE WHAT **YOU** GUYS CAN DO.

EVER SINCE MEL QUIT THE BAND, ALL THEY DO IS ARGUE.

I JUST DON'T GET IT.

A FEW DAYS EARLIER...

WHERE'S MEL? WE ONLY HAVE TWO HOURS.

?

IT'S GOTTEN A LOT WORSE SINCE THAT LAST BAND PRACTICE.

I REALLY HATE THAT. WHY DOESN'T SHE DO WHAT SHE SAYS?

SHE'S BEEN ACTING REALLY WEIRD LATELY.

SOMETHING'S MESSED UP.

MEL! FINALLY YOU'RE HERE! LET'S GET STARTED.

WE'RE GOING TO PLAY "STEP UP".

DID YOU WORK ON THE LYRICS?

. . . . .

NO, I DIDN'T DO ANYTHING.

WHAT'S GOING ON?

WHY NOT?

WAIT!

THIS IS BAD NEWS. THOSE TWO ARE NEVER GOING TO BE FRIENDS AGAIN.

IT MUST BE A "GIRL THING."

LOVE, HATE, LOVE, HATE...

IT'S TOO MUCH FOR ME. I JUST PLAY DRUMS AND SKATE.

GUYS RULE!

DON'T MAKE ME LAUGH!

YOU KNOW I'M BETTER THAN YOU.

GO FIND SOMEPLACE ELSE TO SKATE!

DO YOU THINK THEY'RE GOING TO START PULLING EACH OTHER'S HAIR OUT?

47 命

NO! HELP!
NO!
I'M SINKING!

WHAT'S HAPPENING?
WHOSE VOICE
IS THAT?

THE QUEEN!

I'LL NEVER
FORGIVE
HER...

NEVER!

WHAT IS THIS PLACE?

SOME KIND OF CAVE?

53 龍

WHAT'S THAT SOUND?

IT'S COMING FROM DEEP INSIDE.

???

YOUNG MAN, YOU MUST ACCEPT YOUR FATE.

YOU MUST SERVE URO. I NOW DUB YOU CAPTAIN ACIDULOUS.

YOU'RE KILLING ME!

TAKE THIS NEW POWER INTO YOUR VEINS!

FIGHT ALONGSIDE US.

HOW CAN I HELP HIM?

DON THE MASK OF OBEDIENCE!

WOW!

WOW!

HELP ME!!

THAT'S THE WEIRDEST DREAM I EVER HAD. I HAVE TO GET OUT OF HERE....

HE KEPT SHOUTING FOR HELP...

IT SCARED ME TO DEATH.

YEAH, WRAPPED AROUND THIS KID. THEY WERE STRANGLING HIM.

IN A CAVE, RIGHT?

THERE WERE ALL THESE SNAKES...

THAT'S WHAT HAPPENED TO ME.

EXACTLY THE SAME THING!

HEY, DOUG... NAOMI!

IT ALL HAPPENED SO FAST. FIRST, I WAS IN THE LOT...

...AND THEN I WAS BEING PULLED DOWN INTO SOME SLIMY CAVE.

IT WAS SOOO COLD.

MEL, WHEN DID YOU GET HERE?

IT TOTALLY CREEPED ME OUT! LOOK GUYS, I DON'T KNOW WHAT'S GOING ON HERE BUT I'M REALLY SORR...

UH! WHAT WAS THAT?

SPLURP

DID YOU SEE THOSE DISGUSTING SNAKES IN YOUR DREAMS?

YEAH, I DID.

Creeeeeeeeeeeeeeee..........eeeeeepy

WHAT THE...!!?

WHAT'S GOING ON?

DID YOU HEAR SOMETHING?

Creeeeeeeee.........eeeepy

YEAH!

Hwooh

?

KABOOM

......?

SHE JUST DISAPPEARED!

......

SO WHAT ARE WE SUPPOSED TO DO WITH THIS STRANGE THING?

......

I'M NOT A THING. I'M A SQUELP.

WHY ME!?

SAY SOMETHING TO HIM, NAOMI.

HE CAN SPEAK!

ONLY YOU CAN HELP US....

...ONLY YOU CAN SAVE YOUR FRIEND.

FOLLOW ME!

WHO WERE THEY? AND WHERE DID THEY TAKE MEL?

WHAT'S GOING ON? WE DON'T GET IT.

REPORTING, MY CAPTAIN.

!

DID YOU GET HER?

OF COURSE. HERE SHE IS.

ドガ

SHE CANNOT ESCAPE FROM THIS BUBBLE.

GRAAARR!!

....?

DO YOU SEE THIS FOREST? I MADE IT TOO. I GROW MORE POWERFUL WITH YOUR HELP.

YOU'VE GOT THE MAGIC, SATORIN. WHICH WAY NOW?

?

Keeeeeeeeee eeeeeeeeee

WHAT'S WRONG, DOUG?

.....?

I DON'T KNOW.... I CAN'T...

AGH, MY EARS... THAT RINGING...

YOUNG WARRIOR! COME TO ME!

NAOMI, SOMETHING'S UP WITH DOUG.

I'VE GOT YOU, MAN! COME ON, SIT DOWN.

WHO'S CALLING HIM?

IT MUST BE ONE OF THE SPIRITS. NO ONE CAN ESCAPE THE CALL.

!??

I DON'T KNOW EXACTLY. I ONLY KNOW I FEEL FORCES FROM MY WORLD.

WHERE IS YOUR WORLD, SATORIN?

A PLACE FAR AWAY. A PLACE I DON'T REMEMBER WELL.

BUT WHAT DOES THIS SPIRIT WANT WITH DOUG?

がさがさ
swish
swish
swish

!?

I cannot say. It's all confused.

あわわ

IS HE BEING KIDNAPPED? ARE THEY TAKING HIM TO MEL?

SHUT UP!

WHAT IS THE NAME OF YOUR TRIBE?

WE'RE FROM BLUE STAR. WE'VE COME TO HELP YOU.

JIM, WHAT ARE YOU SAYING?

YES... I BELIEVE WE HAVE BEEN WAITING FOR YOU.

HOLD ON A SECOND.

Ouch

JIM IS TELLING THE TRUTH.

DON'T BE SO STUPID!

BUT I'M SURE IT'S TRUE.

DON'T LIE TO HER.

IS YOUR FRIEND SICK? MAYBE I CAN HELP.

THIS IS SERIOUS!

LISTEN, SATORIN, WHAT IS REALLY GOING ON HERE?

BUT... IT'S TRUE...

AACKKK...

DOES SHE HAVE MEDICINE?

?

MY GRANDMOTHER IS A GREAT HEALER. SHE IS THE ELDER OF OUR VILLAGE.

WE CAN BRING HIM TO HER.

!!! ♥

DON'T WORRY. I'LL BE BACK VERY SOON.

DOUG, CAN YOU HEAR ME?

YOU MUST COME AND SEE FOR YOURSELF.

HOW DO WE CARRY HIM THERE?

YESSS!

I WILL RUN TO OUR VILLAGE AND GET MY FRIENDS TO HELP.

DOUG, WAKE UP! WHERE HAVE THESE SPIRITS TAKEN YOU?

I SURE HOPE RAINBOW DOESN'T TAKE TOO LONG.

.....

....?

WHERE AM I? WHAT KIND OF PLACE IS THIS?

AGHH...

ARE THEY REALLY SILVER?

THESE PILLARS...

WHERE ARE YOU, GUYS?

WARRIOR!

NAOMI!?

JIM?

I'VE NEVER SEEN ANYTHING LIKE THIS!

JIM?

AAAH!

...G

D...G

OUCH!

WAIT!!

FORGET IT. YOU'RE AWAKE. THAT'S THE IMPORTANT THING.

YOU HAD ME WORRIED.

WHAT HAPPENED TO ME? ALL I CAN REMEMBER IS THIS RINGING IN MY EAR....

MY JAW.

S-SORRY

YOU HAD US SCARED TO DEATH.

DOUG!?

SORRY.... I WAS JUST...

YOU'RE AWAKE.

...DREAMING, I GUESS. WHERE ARE WE?

THIS IS PRINCESS RAINBOW'S HOUSE. SHE LIVES HERE WITH HER GRANDMOTHER, GRINDA.

THE VILLAGERS CARRIED YOU HERE. THEY'VE BEEN LOOKING AFTER US.

MIND YOUR OWN BUSINESS, UNLESS YOU WANT TO HEAR MORE RINGING.

SHE'S VERY BEAUTIFUL!

WE'RE GLAD TO BE HERE. WE ARE HERE TO HELP IN ANY WAY WE CAN.

...?

THANK YOU. I'M SURE IT'S DELICIOUS.

THIS IS A GREAT DELICACY OF THE POTONAWI. THE FEET OF THE FISH ARE THE BEST PART.

!?

!!

YUCK!

???

ER...

Cut it out!!

Our hosts have brought this!!

Eat it!!

NO WAY! A FISH WITH LEGS?

DELICIOUS, RIGHT?

RAINBOW, HAVE YOU SEEN OUR FRIEND, SATORIN? YOU KNOW, THAT LITTLE GUY WHO WAS WITH US?

GROSS!!

YES, HE IS WITH MY GRANDMOTHER. THEY SEEM TO HAVE MUCH TO TALK ABOUT.

.....

WILL YOU KEEP IT DOWN BACK THERE?! YOU'RE GOING TO GET US THROWN OUT OF HERE!

唯 124

HEY, WATCH WHERE YOU'RE GOING!

RAINBOW, THAT FISH WAS CRAZY! YOU WANT TO GO GET SOME ICE CREAM WITH ME?

I'M SORRY. THEY CAN BE SO RUDE.

ICE CREAM? THE POTONAWI DON'T KNOW THIS "ICE CREAM", BUT WE COULD WALK TO THE RIVER AND...

JIM, YOU'RE ACTING LIKE A JERK. BACK OFF.

Jim

HEY, RAINBOW, I DON'T GET IT. DOES YOUR GRANDMOTHER KNOW SATORIN?

127 魔

AND NOW URO HAS MEL!

HE SENT HIS SOLDIERS TO OUR WORLD TO CAPTURE HER. BUT WHY?

IF HE TOOK THEIR FRIEND, THEY MUST BE THE WARRIORS CHOSEN TO FIGHT HIM.

URO WAS IN BLUE STAR?

FRIENDS FROM BLUE STAR...

THE ELDER REQUESTS THE HONOR OF YOUR PRESENCE.

OK THEN, LET'S GO!

I'M SURE MY GRANDMOTHER WILL HELP YOU FIND YOUR FRIEND! SHE IS ONE OF THE FOUR WISE ONES OF THE TURTLE REALM.

MY PLEDGE!

Clink

??

NICE VILLAGE!

WAY COOL.

WE MUST SEEM LIKE MARTIANS TO THEM. ESPECIALLY JIM.

WHY ARE ALL THESE PEOPLE STARING AT US? DO I HAVE A BOOGER COMING OUT OF MY NOSE?

Do you like skateboarding?

What's that?

Tap

Tap Tap

WHAT IS IT, SWEETIE?

!?

THEY SAY YOU HAVE COME TO HELP US FROM BEYOND THE STARS.

CAN YOU HELP US?

I'M AFRAID OF THE DARK. THEY SAY THAT SOON EVERYTHING WILL BE COVERED IN DARKNESS.

誠 132

DON'T WORRY, AZSTAR. THEY HAVE COME TO HELP US.

RAINBOW...

WELL...

REALLY?

WE LOVE YOU.

TAKE THIS.

IT'S ALL RIGHT. WE WANT TO HELP THEM.

I'M SORRY. ALL OF THE CHILDREN ARE VERY WORRIED.

YEAH, WHAT NAOMI?

HEY, JIM...

NOW, PLEASE COME AND MEET MY GRANDMOTHER.

SURE...

'CAUSE THE LAST TIME I LOOKED, WE WERE JUST THREE SKATERS WITH A BAND FROM UNION CITY.

......

DO YOU REALLY BELIEVE WE'RE THE ONES THEY'VE BEEN WAITING FOR?

MAYBE?
WHO KNOWS...? BUT...

.....

...SINCE WE HAVE
TO FIND MEL,

WE MIGHT AS WELL
HELP THESE PEOPLE
WHILE WE'RE AT IT.

I GUESS YOU'RE
RIGHT... STILL...

MY GRANDMOTHER'S MAGIC PROTECTS OUR VILLAGE.

SHE CALLED UPON THE GREAT MOTHER TO GROW THESE MOUNTAINS. SO FAR, URO'S FORCES HAVE NOT BEEN ABLE TO BREACH OUR DEFENSES.

THIS IS THE TENT OF MEETINGS. IT IS A SACRED PLACE.

WOW, YOUR GRANDMA SOUNDS INCREDIBLE. MINE CAN MAKE A WICKED APPLE PIE, BUT THAT'S ABOUT IT.

32! That's a lot of magic.

SHE IS GRINDA, THE THIRTY-SECOND IN A LINE OF POTONAWI MAGICIANS THAT GOES BACK TO THE TIME OF OUR GREAT MOTHER.

SHE AWAITS YOU.

THE
TIGER?

女教皇 138

MEET SATORIN'S NEW FRIEND, GRINDA. SHE IS GOING TO HELP US. SHE UNDERSTANDS.

WELCOME. SATORIN HAS TOLD ME MUCH ABOUT YOU.

YOU ARE DOUG, ARE YOU NOT?

ER... YES, MA'AM.

!?!

I KNOW, BUT YOU HAVE BEEN BROUGHT HERE FOR A HIGHER PURPOSE.

YOU HAVE SEEN RAITETSU BEFORE, HAVEN'T YOU?

I DON'T GET IT. AND THAT TIGER...

WHAT'S GOING ON HERE? THIS IS ALL REALLY CONFUSING.

I KNOW, BECAUSE YOUR ARRIVAL HAS BEEN FORETOLD LONG AGO. THERE IS A TASK FOR EACH ONE OF YOU.

SHE'S JOKING, RIGHT?

THAT TIGER?

YOU SAW THAT TIGER?

DOUG HAS BEEN THE FIRST ONE CHOSEN TO FULFILL THE PROPHECY.

THIS IS STRESSING ME OUT!

LET'S HOPE SATORIN KNOWS WHAT HE'S DOING....

SATORIN BROUGHT YOU HERE TO HELP US.

......

WHY WERE YOU CHOSEN FIRST?

YEAH, REALLY, DOUG. WHAT MAKES **YOU** SO SPECIAL?

LOOK AT THE PENDANT. THE PLEDGE OF THE SILVER TIGER REVEALS ALL.

141 教皇

HERE... LET'S SEE IT.

WHEN I WOKE UP, IT WAS AROUND MY NECK.

RAITETSU GAVE YOU A MISSION, DID HE NOT?

YES, MRS. GRINDA.

HE SAID IT WAS MY JOB TO FREE HIM. HE SAID I MUST FIND THE MIRROR SHRINE AND RELEASE HIM FROM IT TO GET HIS POWER.

NOW I KEEP HEARING HIS VOICE IN MY HEAD.

IT WAS SO WEIRD. THERE WAS THIS BIG HALL WITH SILVER PILLARS. HE CALLED ME HIS SON.

AMAZING...

THIS IS OUR TURTLE REALM.

AND THIS IS THE PLANET OF VERMONIA, HOME OF OUR GREAT MOTHER.

EVERYTHING HERE MOVED IN HARMONY TOGETHER UNTIL HER TWO MOST TRUSTED SUBJECTS...

...TWO BROTHERS, URO AND BOROS, FOUGHT AGAINST EACH OTHER: ONE TO DEFEND HER KINGDOM, AND THE OTHER TO SEIZE IT.

女帝

BUT WHY DID URO SUDDENLY REBEL AGAINST HIS QUEEN? WHAT MADE HIM SO ANGRY?

HE WANTED HER POWER. HE HOPED TO RULE THROUGH POSSESSION OF THE SACRED BOLIRIUM. IT IS WRITTEN THAT WHOEVER POSSESSES THE BOLIRIUM OF VERMONIA CONTROLS THE EBB AND FLOW OF ALL THINGS.

URO WAS WILLING TO KILL HIS OWN BROTHER TO BE KING.

THE WAR RAGED ON FOR YEARS AND YEARS...

...BATTLE AFTER BATTLE. MANY LIVES WERE LOST.

EVENTUALLY, URO'S EVIL FORCES BEGAN TAKING OVER.

YOU MUST NEVER LOSE FAITH IN THE LOVE OF THE GREAT MOTHER, MY GRANDDAUGHTER.

SO, AT LEAST, IT IS WRITTEN... BUT SOMETIMES IT IS HARD TO BELIEVE.

WILL WE EVER RID OURSELVES OF URO?

SO WHERE'S THE BOLIRIUM?

I STILL DON'T UNDERSTAND. WHY US?

PERHAPS IT WOULD BE BEST FOR YOU TO SEE FOR YOURSELVES.

Keeeeeen

WE ARE NOW IN THE MOST SACRED PLACE OF THE POTONAWI:

THE CAVE OF THE QUEEN.

BEHOLD THE PROPHECY. LOOK AT YOUR DESTINY, YOUNG WARRIORS.

INCREDIBLE. IT'S LIKE INDIANA JONES.

HERE WE CAN READ THE MESSAGES FROM THE ANCESTORS, OUR FIRST ELDERS.

NAOMI, IT'S LIKE THOSE EGYPTIAN HIEROGLYPHS. I CAN'T FIGURE ANY OF THIS OUT.

CAN'T YOU SEE YOURSELVES? AND URO COILED READY TO STRIKE?

FOUR OF US...

THERE IS NO DOUBT OF THE TRUTH OF THESE WORDS. YOU MUST AT ALL COSTS AVOID FALLING INTO URO'S HANDS.

EACH OF YOU HAS ONLY IMPERFECT KNOWLEDGE OF THE BOLIRIUM'S LOCATION.

BUT AS WHEN THE PIECES OF A TORN MAP ARE PUT TOGETHER, SO WILL YOUR COMBINED KNOWLEDGE REVEAL THE SECRET.

BUT THEY HAVE NOW BEEN CAPTURED. AND ALSO YOUR FRIEND, THE FOURTH WARRIOR.

THE GUARDIANS WERE SENT IN ADVANCE TO INSTRUCT YOU.

YES...

THIS LEAVES ONLY YOU THREE.

MEL, WHAT ARE THEY DOING TO YOU?

MEL!

WE WILL EITHER ALL TRIUMPH OR PERISH TOGETHER...

AND THE BOLIRIUM WILL BE LOST FOREVER.

YES, IT IS YOUR DESTINY.

WE HAVE TO DO SOMETHING NOW!

THE ROOM HAS SHIFTED AGAIN....

YES, BECAUSE URO'S ARMY IS ATTACKING.

COME AT ONCE!!

PRINCESS RAINBOW!!

WE NEED YOU!!

WAIT HERE, EVERYONE!!

RAINBOW!!

I'M COMING!

JIM, DON'T GO OUT THERE!

RAINBOW, I'M COMING WITH YOU!!

·······

157 カ

RAINBOW, USE YOUR MAGIC!

NO!!

ANCESTORS, HELP ME HOLD THE SPHERE!

COVER AND PROTECT!

LITTLE GIRL, YOU AND YOUR FRIENDS SHOULD GIVE UP. THE TIME FOR GAMES IS OVER.

GRANDMOTHER! HELP ME!

YOUR GRANNY CAN'T HELP YOU NOW.

MY FRIENDS— THEY'RE SO BRAVE.

AMUSING TO WATCH THE YOUNG WARRIOR FIGHT, IS IT NOT?

YOUR FRIEND SHOULDN'T GET TOO COCKY. THERE ARE MUCH NASTIER THINGS TO COME.

.....

Clap

Clap

SIT THERE AND WATCH. IT WON'T BE PRETTY.

I COULD EVEN LET YOU OUT FOR A BETTER VIEW.

I HAVEN'T EXACTLY BEEN TOLD THAT I CAN'T.

WHAT SORT OF STUPID THINGS ARE YOU SAYING, GAZSO?

MY CAPTAIN, I WAS ONLY JOKING.

GET OUT OF HERE.

A SOLDIER OF MINE HAS BEEN DEFEATED, AND I PAY FOR IT EVERY TIME.

WHO'S THAT?

REPORTING FOR DUTY, CAPTAIN ACIDULOUS.

MY CAPTAIN?

NO, STOP!

DON'T TOUCH ME.

MY EYES ARE COVERED WITH THE MASK OF OBEDIENCE. YOUR TOUCH TURNS ALL TO STONE.

WE LIVE, AND DIE, TO SERVE GENERAL URO. THIS IS THE PRIVILEGE WE HAVE BOTH BEEN GRANTED.

YOU KNOW YOUR TOUCH WOULD BE THE END OF ME. WHAT ARE YOU THINKING?

GO NOW. BRING ME THOSE THREE KIDS, EVEN IF THEY COME TO ME AS STATUES.

THEY'RE MONSTERS, AND THEY'RE EVEN MONSTROUS TO EACH OTHER. I'M FRIGHTENED...

...AND SAD FOR THEM TOO.

I WILL AWAIT THEM AT THE MIRROR SHRINE.

WHEW.

I DID IT. HE'S GONE. DEFEATED.

AHH...

NAOMI?

I'VE GOT YOU. YOU'RE GOING TO BE OK.

AGH.

COME ON—STAY WITH ME. TELL ME HOW YOU LEARNED TO THROW THUNDER.

QUICK—I'M GOING TO PASS OUT.

正義 **180**

IT LOOKS LIKE JIM... GOT HIT!

HE'S DEAD!

NO, IT'S OK, RAINBOW'S GOT HIM. THEY'RE TALKING.

WHEW, THEY MADE IT THEN.

!?

Don't move!

YOU GUYS OK?

RAITETSU MUST BE CALLING US. RAINBOW, WHAT'S IN THAT DIRECTION?

LOOK—THE SABERTOOTH IS POINTING ALL BY ITSELF.

THE VALLEY OF NAGOUB. IT IS THERE THAT YOU WILL FIND RAITETSU'S PRISON.

THE VALLEY OF NAGOUB? I BET GRINDA'S MAGIC CAN'T HELP US THERE.

I WILL EXPLAIN. COME TO ME.

DOUG, TRUST IN THE PLEDGE OF RAITETSU. IT WILL GUIDE YOU TO THE MIRROR SHRINE.

AND EVERY STEP WE MAKE TOWARD UNLEASHING THE POWER OF RAITETSU

WILL BRING US ONE STEP CLOSER TO MEL.

Splash

THE MONSTER IS
OF MY BLOOD.

I MUST FIGHT.
I MUST OBEY.

RIGHT YOU ARE.
BUT I CAN TAKE YOUR
MIND OFF SUCH MATTERS
WITH ANOTHER
SAD STORY...

I FEEL
SORRY
FOR HIM.

THE CAPTAIN
IS DYING.

ONE DAY SASSELLA MET A KIND GENERAL WHO PROMISED TO FREE HER FROM HER CURSE IF SHE FOUGHT FOR HIM.

A GIRL WHO CAN NEVER TOUCH HER LOVE!

THAT IS THE MOST TERRIBLE STORY IN THE WORLD.

OBEY AND BE FREE.

SO SASSELLA JOINED URO'S ARMY. YOUR FRIENDS WILL MEET HER AT THE MIRROR SHRINE.

.....

YOU MUST CHOOSE THE WEAPON THAT SUITS YOU BEST.

THESE WEAPONS, LIKE YOUR CLOTHES, CARRY SPELLS. THE POTONAWI HAVE FOUGHT WITH THESE FOR GENERATIONS.

I BRING THE BOW OF MY BROTHER. IT IS BEST TO BE PREPARED.

DO WE REALLY NEED TO CARRY THESE THINGS?

YES, THERE'S BAD STUFF OUT THERE.

HAVE YOU GOT YOUR BOARDS?

WE'LL NEED THEM.

WARRIORS OF BLUE STAR, THE POTONAWI SALUTE YOU AND SEND YOU FORTH WITH OUR PRAYERS.

HAS ANYONE FIGURED OUT HOW WE ARE GOING TO FIND THIS SHRINE?

I SEE ONLY ROCKS AND MORE ROCKS.

THERE USED TO BE A BEAUTIFUL FOREST HERE.

WAIT!
THE TOOTH IS
PULLING ME!

STOP FIGHTING
IT, DOUG.

RAITETSU IS
TELLING YOU
HE'S NEARBY.
STAND STILL.

!?

WAIT UP!

HEY, GUYS!

!?

DOUG, WOW,
THAT THING...

...IT'S ALL
LIT UP.

魂 202

WOW. EVERYTHING'S BEEN CLEARED AWAY.

?? UNBELIEVABLE!

LOOK DOWN!

IT'S A BIG MIRROR. WE MUST NOW BE OVER THE SHRINE.

I CAN SEE MYSELF!

NO, THERE AREN'T EVEN ANY CRACKS.

IS THERE AN ENTRANCE?

道 204

I DON'T SEE ANY WAY TO GET IN.

DON'T WORRY. YOU WON'T BE GOING INSIDE.

WHO IS THAT??!!

Vermonia ②
Call of the Winged Panther

COMING

SOON...